Financial Planning Workbook

to Accompany

Personal Finance

Jeff Madura

Addison
Wesley

Boston San Francisco New York
London Toronto Sydney Tokyo Singapore Madrid
Mexico City Munich Paris Cape Town Hong Kong Montreal

Financial Planning Workbook to Accompany Madura, *Personal Finance*

Copyright © 2002 Pearson Education, Inc.

ISBN: 0-321-09750-5
1 2 3 4 5 6 7 8 9 10-HT-0504030201

Table of Contents

Build Your Own Financial Plan ....Page 1

The Sampsons Family: A Continuing Case ....Page 53

Brad Brooks: A Continuing Case ....Page 75

Build Your Own Financial Plan

Chapter 1: Overview of a Financial Plan

Goals
1. Evaluate your current financial situation
2. Set short-term, intermediate-term, and long-term goals

Analysis
1. Complete the Personal Financial Goals template below.

Personal Financial Goals

Financial Goal Short-Term Goals	Dollar Amount to Accomplish	Priority (Low, Medium, High)
1.		
2.		
3.		
4.		
5.		

Intermediate-Term Goals		
1.		
2.		
3.		
4.		
5.		

Long-Term Goals		
1.		
2.		
3.		
4.		
5.		

Decisions
1. Describe your strategies for reaching the goals you set.

Chapter 2: Planning with Personal Financial Statements

Goals

1. Determine how to increase net cash flows in the near future.
2. Determine how to increase net cash flows in the distant future.

Analysis

1. Prepare your personal cash flow statement.

Personal Cash Flow Statement

Cash Inflows	This Month
Disposable (after-tax) income	_____
Interest on deposits	_____
Dividend payments	_____
Other	_____
Total Cash Inflows	_____
Cash Outflows	
Rent	_____
Cable TV	_____
Electricity and water	_____
Telephone	_____
Groceries	_____
Health care insurance and expenses	_____
Clothing	_____
Car expenses (insurance, maintenance, and gas)	_____
Recreation	_____
Other	_____
Total Cash Outflows	_____
Net Cash Flows	_____

2. Prepare your personal balance sheet.

Personal Balance Sheet

Assets

Liquid Assets	
Cash	
Checking account	
Savings account	
Other liquid assets	
Total liquid assets	
Household Assets	
Home	
Car	
Furniture	
Other household assets	
Total household assets	
Investment Assets	
Stocks	
Bonds	
Mutual Funds	
Other investments	
Total investment assets	
Real Estate	
Residence	
Vacation home	
Other	
Total real estate	
Total Assets	

Liabilities and Net Worth	
Current Liabilities	
Loans	
Credit card balance	
Other current liabilities	
Total current liabilities	
Long-Term Liabilities	
Mortgage	
Car loan	
Other long-term liabilities	
Total long-term liabilities	
Total Liabilities	

Net Worth	

3. Reevaluate the goals you set in chapter 1. Based on your personal cash flow statement, indicate how much you can save each year to reach the goals you set.

Personal Financial Goals

Financial Goal Short-Term Goals	Dollar Amount	Savings per Year	Number of Years)
1.			
2.			
3.			
4.			
5.			

Intermediate-Term Goals

1.			
2.			
3.			
4.			
5.			

Long-Term Goals

1.			
2.			
3.			
4.			
5.			

Decisions

1. Describe the actions you will take to increase your net cash flows in the near future.

2. Detail your plans for increasing your net cash flows in the distant future.

Chapter 3: Applying Time Value Concepts

Goals
1. Determine how much savings you will accumulate by various future points in time.
2. Estimate how much you will need to save each year in order to achieve the goals you have set.

Analysis
1. For each goal you set in chapter 1, make three calculations using an interest rate that you believe you can earn on your invested savings and one higher and one lower than that rate.

Time Value of Money

Future Value of a Present Amount	
Present Value	
Number of Periods	
Interest Rate per Period	
Future Value	

Future Value of an Annuity	
Payment per Period	
Number of Periods	
Interest Rate pre Period	
Future Value	

Present Value of a Future Amount	
Future Value	
Number of Periods	
Interest Rate per Period	
Present Value	

Present Value of an Annuity	
Payment per Period	
Number of Periods	
Interest Rate pre Period	
Present Value	

Personal Financial Goals

Financial Goal Short-Term Goals	Dollar Amount	Rate of Return	Priority (Low, Medium, High)
1.			
2.			
3.			
4.			
5.			

Intermediate-Term Goals

1.			
2.			
3.			
4.			
5.			

Long-Term Goals

1.			
2.			
3.			
4.			
5.			

2. Revise the cash flow statement you created in chapter 2 as necessary to enable you to achieve your goals.

Personal Cash Flow Statement

Cash Inflows	This Month
Disposable (after-tax) income	
Interest on deposits	
Dividend payments	
Other	
Total Cash Inflows	
Cash Outflows	
Rent	
Cable TV	
Electricity and water	
Telephone	
Groceries	
Health care insurance and expenses	
Clothing	
Car expenses (insurance, maintenance, and gas)	
Recreation	
Other	
Total Cash Outflows	
Net Cash Flows	

Decisions

1. Report on how much you must save per year and the return you must earn to meet your goals.

Chapter 4: Using Tax Concepts for Planning

Goals
1. Reduce taxable income (thereby reducing taxes paid) to the extent allowable by the IRS.
2. Reduce taxes paid by deferring income.

Analysis
Gross income: _____
Tax liability: _____

1. For each of the goals you established in chapter 1, indicate tax advantage options that may enable you to increase your deductions and/or reduce your gross income.

Personal Financial Goals

Financial Goal Short-Term Goals	Dollar Amount	Rate of Return	Priority (Low, Medium, High)	Tax Advantage Options
1.				
2.				
3.				
4.				
5.				

Intermediate-Term Goals				
1.				
2.				
3.				
4.				
5.				

Long-Term Goals				
1.				
2.				
3.				
4.				
5.				

2. If you are considering hiring a tax preparer, use the following questions as an interview guide to screen candidates.

Answers

(1) How long have you been preparing tax returns?

(2) What training have you had in the preparation of tax returns?

    College degrees earned:

    Tax training courses:

    Certifications:

(3) How long have you worked for this organization?

(4) Do you carry professional liability insurance?

(5) Is this your full-time job?

(6) If I am audited, are you authorized to represent me before the IRS?

(7) How many hours of continuing professional education are you required to have each year to maintain your employment?

(8) How many tax returns do you prepare a year?

(9) What type of software does your firm use to prepare returns?

(10) What percentage of the returns done by you have been audited?

Decisions

1. Describe the actions you will take to achieve tax savings in the present year.

2. Detail the means by which you will reduce your tax liability in the future.

Chapter 5: Banking and Interest Rates

Goals
1. Identify the banking services that are most important to you.
2. Determine which financial institution will provide you with the best banking services.

Analysis

1. Evaluate what banking services are most important to you with a score of "10" for the most important and "1" for the least. Then evaluate five financial institutions with respect to the services offered; rate the institutions from "5" as the best for that service to "1" as the worst. The template will calculate scores for each institution.

Banking Services Scorecard

SERVICES OFFERED	Priority	INSTITUTION 1		INSTITUTION 2		INSTITUTION 3		INSTITUTION 4		INSTITUTION 5	
		Rank	Score	Rank	Score	Rank	Score	Rank	Score	Rank	Score
1. Hours of operations - evenings, Saturdays											
2. Locations - proximity to work and home											
3. Fees/Minimum balance for checking accounts											
4. Fees for ATM usage											
5. Interest rate on savings accounts											
6. Interest rate on checking accounts											
7. VISA/Master Card available and annual fee											
8. Interest rate on home loans											
9. Interest rate on car loans											
10. Safety deposit boxes and rental rates											
TOTAL SCORE FOR EACH INSTITUTION											

Decisions

1. Describe the services and characteristics that are of prime importance to you in a financial institution.

2. Which of the financial institutions you evaluated is most optimal for your needs? Why?

Chapter 6: Managing Your Money

Goals
1. Maintain sufficient liquidity to ensure that all your anticipated bills are paid on time.
2. Maintain sufficient liquidity so that you can cover unanticipated expenses.
3. Invest any excess funds in deposits that offer the highest return while ensuring liquidity.

Analysis
1. Review the cash flow statement you prepared in chapter 3 and assess your liquidity.
2. Evaluate the short-term goals you created in chapter 1 as high, medium, or low with respect to liquidity, risk, fees/minimum balance, and return.

Short-term Goal Prioritization of Factors

SHORT-TERM GOAL	LIQUIDITY	RISK	FEES/MINIMUM BALANCE	RETURN

3. Rank each of the money market investments as good, fair, or poor with respect to liquidity, risk, fees/minimum balance, and return.

MONEY MARKET INVESTMENT	LIQUIDITY	RISK	FEES/MINIMUM BALANCE	RETURN
Checking Account				
NOW Account				
Savings Account				
Money Market Deposit Account (MMDA)				
Certificate of Deposit				
Treasury Bill				
Money Market Fund				
Asset Management Account				

Decisions

1. Describe how you will ensure adequate liquidity to cover anticipated expenses.

2. Detail how you will ensure liquidity to meet unanticipated expenses.

3. Explain which money market investments will be most effective in reaching your short-term goals.

Chapter 7: Managing Your Credit

Goals
1. Evaluate your credit report.
2. Determine your overall creditworthiness.
3. Set a policy to avoid incurring high interest expenses on credit cards.

Analysis
1. Obtain a copy of your credit report from www.transunion.com or www.creditbase.com, scrutinize the report, and report any inaccuracies to the credit bureaus.
2. Using the MSN homepage, determine your overall creditworthiness. At www.msn.com, click on the tab entitled "Money" and then click on "Savings and Spending." When the Saving and Spending page comes up, go to the section entitled "More Tools" on the left. Click on the debt evaluator in this section and follow the instructions.
3. Referring to your personal cash flow statement, determine how much excess cash inflows you have each month. Based on this amount, set a self-imposed credit limit for each month so that you can pay your balance off in full. Use the following template to select a credit card with favorable terms. Rate the cards from five being the best in an area to one being the worst.

Bank Credit Card Scorecard

QUESTION	CREDIT CARD ISSUER				
	1	2	3	4	5
1. Annual fee					
2. Interest rate on purchases					
3. Interest rate on cash advances					
4. Transaction fee for cash advances					
5. Insurance on purchases					
6. Credit earned toward purchases at selected businesses					
7. Frequent flyer miles					
8. Free delivery on mail order purchases					
9. Phone card capability					
10. Credit limit available					
11					
12					
13					
14					
15					
TOTAL					

Decisions

1. Are there any errors on your credit report that you must correct? How can you improve your creditworthiness?

2. What is your self-imposed credit limit? What credit card offers the most favorable terms for your needs?

Chapter 8: Personal Loans

Goals
1. Limit your personal financing to a level and maturity that you can pay back on a timely basis.
2. For loans you anticipate needing in the future, evaluate the advantages and disadvantages of lenders.
3. Compare the cost of buying and leasing a car.

Analysis
1. Review your personal cash flow statement. How much can you afford to pay each month for personal loans?
2. Identify several prospective lenders for personal loans you may need in the future. What are the advantages and disadvantages of each source with respect to the interest rates offered, method of calculating interest, other criteria of importance to you.

Loan Evaluation

Loan One

DESCRIPTION OF LOAN	SOURCES FOR LOAN	ADVANTAGES OF SOURCE	DISADVANTAGES OF SOURCE
	1.		
	2.		
	3.		

Loan Two

DESCRIPTION OF LOAN	SOURCES FOR LOAN	ADVANTAGES OF SOURCE	DISADVANTAGES OF SOURCE
	1.		
	2.		
	3.		

Loan Three

DESCRIPTION OF LOAN	SOURCES FOR LOAN	ADVANTAGES OF SOURCE	DISADVANTAGES OF SOURCE
	1.		
	2.		
	3.		

Loan Four

DESCRIPTION OF LOAN	SOURCES FOR LOAN	ADVANTAGES OF SOURCE	DISADVANTAGES OF SOURCE
	1.		
	2.		
	3.		

3. Compare the cost of purchasing a car versus leasing a car over a 4-year period.

Cost of Purchasing Versus Leasing a Car

Cost of Purchasing the Car
Down payment
Interest rate _____
Number of months _____
Annual forgone interest on down payment _____
Monthly payment on car loan _____
Total monthly payments _____
Total cost of purchasing **_____**
Expected amount to be received when car is sold _____
Total cost **_____**

Cost of Leasing the Car
Security deposit
Forgone interest _____
Monthly lease payments _____
Total monthly payments _____
Total cost _____

Decisions
1. Report how much you can afford to spend each month on personal loans.

2. Report which lenders you may consider using in the future and why.

3. For your needs, is purchasing or leasing a vehicle a better choice?

Chapter 9: Purchasing and Financing a Home

Goals
1. Limit the amount of mortgage financing to an affordable level; determine if homeownership or renting is better financially.
2. Select the shortest loan maturity with affordable monthly payments.
3. Select the mortgage loan type (fixed or adjustable rate) that is most likely to result in the lowest interest expenses.

Analysis
1. Search listings of homes for sale in your price range on the MSN Web site (www.msn.com).

	From	To
Price Range:		
Zip Code:		

Potential Homes

ADDRESS	LIST PRICE	MSN PRICE ESTIMATE	MONTHLY PAYMENT	REALTOR

2. Compare the monthly payment estimates to the amount of money you are currently paying for rent. Determine the amount of a down payment you can afford to make.

    Down payment _____

3. Using the MSN web site, gather information on loan terms for both fixed rate and adjustable rate mortgages.

    Expected mortgage amount _____

Prospective Lenders: Fixed-rate Mortgage

FINANCIAL INSTITUTION	INTEREST RATE	MATURITY	CLOSING COSTS	MONTHLY PAYMENT

Prospective Lenders: Adjustable-rate Mortgage

FINANCIAL INSTITUTION	INTEREST RATE	MATURITY	CLOSING COSTS	MONTHLY PAYMENT

4. Create an amortization table for the fixed-rate mortgage that is most affordable.

Loan Amount   _____
Number of Years   _____
Annual Interest Rate_____
Monthly Payment   _____

Amortization Schedule for Year 1

Monthly Payment	Payment	Principal	Interest	Balance

Compare the allocation of principal versus interest paid per year on the loan.

Amortization Schedule (Annual Totals)

Annual Payments	Total Payments	Principal	Interest	Balance
1				
2				
3				
4				
5				
6				
7				
8				
9				
10				
11				
12				
13				
14				
15				
16				
17				
18				
19				
20				
21				
22				
23				
24				
25				
26				
27				
28				
29				
30				
31				
32				
33				
34				
35				
36				
37				
38				
39				
40				

5. Select the mortgage with the best terms. Compare the cost of buying a home with these mortgage terms to renting over a 3-year period.

Renting Versus Owning a Home

Cost of Renting

	Per Month	Amount Per Year	Total over Three Years
Rent			
Renter's Insurance			
Opportunity cost of security deposit			
Total cost of renting			

Cost of Owning

	Per Month	Amount Per Year	Total over Three Years
Mortgage payment			
Down payment			
Opportunity cost of down payment			
Property taxes			
Home insurance			
Closing costs			
Maintenance costs			
Total costs before tax benefits			
Tax savings on:			
Interest payments			
Property taxes			
Points (first year only)			
Total tax savings			
Equity investment			
Increase in home value			
Value of equity			
Cost of purchasing home over three years			

Decisions

1. What is the mortgage amount and down payment that you can afford?

2. Is a fixed-rate or adjustable-rate mortgage better suited to your financial situation? What maturity, interest rate, and monthly payment can you afford?

3. Describe whether homeownership or renting is preferable for you.

Chapter 10: Basics for Investing in Stocks

Goals
1. Determine whether to buy stock.
2. Determine what kinds of stock you should purchase to meet your financial goals.

Analysis
1. Review your cash flow statement to determine how much you can afford to invest in stocks each month.
2. Evaluate your risk tolerance to see if your temperament is suited to the uncertainty of stock investments.

Risk Tolerance Quiz

Answer True or False by entering an X in the appropriate box.

	TRUE	FALSE
(1) If I own stock, I will check its price at least daily if not more often.		
(2) When driving on an interstate, and traffic and weather permit, I never drive in excess of the posted speed limit.		
(3) If the price of my stock declines, my first reaction is to sell		
(4) Another stock market crash similar to 1929 could occur very unexpectedly.		
(5) When I fly in less than perfect weather, I tend to get nervous and concerned about my safety.		
(6) If I sold a stock at a loss of more than 25%, it would greatly shake my confidence in my ability to invest.		
(7) I intensely dislike blind dates.		
(8) When I travel, I write down a packing list to be sure that I don't forget anything.		
(9) When traveling with others, I prefer to do the driving.		
(10) Before buying stock I would want to talk to at least two other people to confirm my choice.		

Results

0-3 True: You have the risk tolerance to invest in individual common stocks.

4-6 True: You would be a nervous investor, but with more knowledge and a few successes, you could probably raise your risk tolerance to a level suitable for common stock investing. Mutual funds might prove a good starting point for your level of risk tolerance.

7-10 True: You are a very conservative and risk intolerant investor that is probably better suited to a bond portfolio.

3. Determine whether stock investments will help you to achieve your short-term, intermediate-term, and long-term goals. Complete the template below for the short-, intermediate-, and long-term goals that you have established and reviewed throughout the course. In determining whether stock is suitable for each goal, take into consideration the timeline for accomplishing the goal, the critical nature of the goal, and, of course, the results of your risk tolerance test. For those goals that you determine stocks are not suitable for, enter an "N" in column three, and do not complete the rest of the line for that goal. If, however, you enter a "Y" in column three, think about the kind of stock that you have selected, but also justify your selection of stocks as a means to accomplish this goal.

Short-Term Goals	SUITABLE? Yes or No	TYPE OF STOCK	JUSTIFICATION
1.			
2.			
3.			
4.			
5.			

Intermediate-Term Goals	SUITABLE? Yes or No	TYPE OF STOCK	JUSTIFICATION
1.			
2.			
3.			
4.			
5.			

Long-Term Goals	SUITABLE? Yes or No	TYPE OF STOCK	JUSTIFICATION
1.			
2.			
3.			
4.			
5.			

Decisions

1. Describe your reasoning for either investing or not investing in stock. If you decide to invest in stocks, how much will you invest each month? What types of stocks will you purchase?

Chapter 11: Return and Risk from Investing in Stocks

Goals
1. Determine how to value a stock based on information about the economy and the firm.

Analysis
1. Select a stock in which you are considering investing.
2. Go to the web site www.federalreserve.gov/FOMC/BeigeBook/2001. Click on the most current report indicated and read the summary. As you do so, keep in mind the product and/or service provided by the company you have selected to analyze. In the space provided below, record your analysis of the Beige Book's economic analysis and its impact on your stock.

Comments

3. Go to the Web site www.smartmoney.com. At the top of the home page you will see a box that says "Enter name or symbol." Enter the name or symbol of the company you wish to analyze and hit "go." This will bring up the "Snapshot" tab for your company. Answer the following questions, finding the data in the tab indicated:

Snapshot

(1) Is the price of your stock currently close to its 52 week high or 52 week low? _____

(2) Does this stock pay a dividend and, if so, how much? _____

Charting

(3) What has been the long-term price trend of your company's stock?

News

(4) Do you see any significant news events that may favorably or unfavorably affect your stock?

[   ]

Earnings

(5) How well has your company met its earnings estimates?

[   ]

(6) How does your company's estimated growth for the current and next fiscal year compare to industry projections?

[   ]

(7) How does your company's estimated growth for the current and next fiscal year compare to the S&P 500?

[   ]

(8) How does your company's estimated three-five year annual growth compare to the industry projections?

[   ]

(9) How does your company's estimated three-five year annual growth compare to the S&P 500?

[   ]

Ratings

(10) How many Wall Street analysts rate your stock? _____

(11) What has been the net change in recommendation? _____

(12) How many rate your stock:
  Strong buy   _____
  Moderate buy   _____
  Hold   _____
  Moderate sell   _____
  Strong sell   _____

(13) How do the recommendations for your stock compare to others in the industry?

+--+
| |
| |
| |
| |
+--+

Competition

(14) How does your company compare, in terms of market value, to its competition, i.e., is it one of the larger or smaller companies in its industry?

+--+
| |
| |
| |
| |
+--+

(15) How does your company's net profit margin compare to that to its competition, i.e., is it one of the larger or smaller companies in its industry?

+--+
| |
| |
| |
| |
+--+

(16) How does your company's net profit margin compare to that of its competition?

+--+
| |
| |
| |
| |
+--+

Key Ratios

(17) How does your company's return on equity compare to that of the industry?

+--+
| |
| |
| |
| |
+--+

(18) How does your company's assets compare to that of the industry?

+--+
| |
| |
| |
| |
+--+

Financials

(19) How does the growth in revenues of your company compare to that of its competition?

```

```

(20) How does the growth in net earnings of your company compare to that of its competition?

```

```

Insiders

(21) In analyzing any stock, it is always good to know what the "insiders" are doing.From the chart, are they buying, selling, intending to buy, or doing nothing?

```

```

Summary
(22) Based on your analysis of the above, answer the following questions:

A. Would this stock be considered (enter an X to signify your choice):

Growth stock   _____
Income stock   _____
Growth/income stock   _____

B. For which of the intermediate or long-term goals that you established in chapter 1 would this stock be a suitable investment, if any?

Intermediate-Term Goals	Suitable? Yes or No	Rationale for Selection
1.		
2.		
3.		
4.		
5.		

Long-Term Goals	Suitable? Yes or No	Rationale for Selection
1.		
2.		
3.		
4.		
5.		

Decisions

1. Based on your valuation, will you purchase this stock?

2. If you invest in this particular stock, which of your financial goals will the investment be aimed at achieving?

Chapter 12: How to Purchase Stocks

Goals

1. Determine a method to use for investing in stocks.

Analysis

1. Answer the following questions to gain a clear picture of your investing assistance needs.

(1) Do you anticipate purchasing individual stocks or bonds or will your portfolio focus on mutual funds? (Mutual funds can be purchased directly without the aid of a broker.)

(2) Do you anticipate actively trading (more than 20 transactions per month) or will you primarily invest with a buy and hold strategy? (Most on-line trading is not cost effective unless you have a certain number of transactions per month, usually exceeding 20.)

(3) Do you anticipate doing yourself whatever research is necessary for your investment decisions or do you anticipate relying on the advice of an investment counselor or research department of a brokerage firm?

Helpful Hint: If your answers to the questions above were that you are going to invest in individual stocks (question 1), you are going to have less than 20 transactions per month (question 2), and/or that you will need at least some advice from a financial advisor or research department, then you probably require the services of a broker.

2. Consider the pros and cons of the various stock investment methods for your situation. Write your conclusions in the right-hand column.

Investment Methods	Comments
Rely on my valuation methods	
Invest in mutual funds	
Invest in publicly-traded indexes	
Rely on investment advisors	

3. If you decide to rely on investment advisors, use the following questions as an interview guide when screening prospective advisors.

Question	Broker 1	Broker 2	Broker 3
1. How long have you been with this firm?			
2. How long have you been in the brokerage business?			
3. What is the average size of the portfolios of your clients?			
4. What is the average cost of a 100-share transaction? (This question will lead to an explanation of the firm's fee structure.)			
5. Does your firm sell no-load mutual funds?			
6. What is the annual maintenance fee for an IRA?			
7. Can I access my account and execute transactions on-line?			
8. Does your firm have services such as check writing, debit card, etc. available?			
9. How many offices does your firm have around the country?			
10. How often do I get statements on my account?			
11. What is the current rate paid on your money market accounts?			
12.			
13.			
14.			
15.			
16.			

Add to this list any questions that are unique to your investing situation and delete any that do not pertain to you.

Decisions

1. What stock investment methods will you make use of?

Chapter 13: Investing in Bonds

Goals
1. Determine if you could benefit from investing in bonds.
2. If you decide to invest in bonds, determine what strategy to use.

Analysis
1. Go to the SmartMoney Web site (www.smartmoney.com) and click on "Economy and Bonds." This will bring you to a page on bond investing that contains numerous articles that you should review to determine if bonds are suitable for your portfolio considering your financial goals. Review these articles in detail, particularly the one entitled *A Bond Primer*.
2. Go to the Web site www.investinginbonds.com. Click on the "Investor's Checklist." Answer the basic questions given and review the perspective to the right of each question.

After completing your visits to the Web sites above, carefully consider whether any of your financial goals could be met with bond investing.

Short-Term Goals	Use Bonds (Yes or No)	Rationale
1.		
2.		
3.		
4.		
5.		

Intermediate-Term Goals	Use Bonds (Yes or No)	Rationale
1.		
2.		
3.		
4.		
5.		

Long-Term Goals	Use Bonds (Yes or No)	Rationale
1.		
2.		
3.		
4.		
5.		

3. Consider the suitability of the following bond investment strategies for your financial situation. Enter your conclusions in the right-hand column.

Strategy to Invest in Bonds	Opinion
1. Interest Rate Strategy	
2. Passive Strategy	
3. Maturity Matching Strategy	

4. Review your personal cash flow statement. If you decide bonds are a good investment, allocate money for them.

Personal Cash Flow Statement

Cash Inflows	**This Month**
Disposable (after-tax) income	
Interest on deposits	
Dividend payments	
Other	
Total Cash Inflows	
Cash Outflows	
Rent	
Cable TV	
Electricity and water	
Telephone	
Groceries	
Health care insurance and expenses	
Clothing	
Car expenses (insurance, maintenance, and gas)	
Recreation	
Other	
Total Cash Outflows	
Net Cash Flows	

Decisions

1. Describe your rationale for investing or not investing in bonds.

2. If you decide to invest in bonds, what strategy will you use?

Chapter 14: Investing in Mutual Funds

Goals
1. Determine if and how you could benefit from investing in mutual funds.
2. If you decide to invest in mutual funds, choose the best types of funds for your needs.

Analysis
1. At www.smartmoney.com, click on the tab marked "Funds". Under the heading "Tools and Research," go to the "Fund Portfolio Builder." Choose two to three that meet your goal needs. Enter your findings in the following chart:

Type of Stock Mutual Funds	Opinion	Goal Suitable For
Growth		
Capital Appreciation		
Equity Income		
Balance Growth and Income		
Sector		
Internet		
Index		
International		

Type of Bond Mutual Fund	Opinion	Goal Suitable For
Treasury		
Ginnie Mae		
Corporate Bond		
High-Yield Bond		
Municipal Bond		
Index Bond		
International Bond		

2. Return to www.smartmoney.com At the "Main Fund" page, go to the "Best Worst" top 25 section. Under the Top 25 funds, select the category of funds you identified as meeting one or more of your goals from the pull-down menu. Answer the following questions and note other pertinent information about your fund:

(1) On the "snap-shot" tab, what is the risk versus return relationship for your fund?

(2) On the "return" tab, how does your fund's return compare to the return for its category over various time spans?

(3) On the "expense" tab, what are the expenses for your fund?

(4) How do your fund's expenses compare to the expenses for this category?

(5) Under the "purchase" tab, is this fund open to new investors?

(6) If so, what is the minimum purchase?

(7) What is the minimum subsequent purchase?

(8) Under the "portfolio" tab, how long has the fund manager been in place?

Decisions

1. What is your decision regarding mutual funds? Why are they/aren't they a good investment for you?

2. If you decide to invest in mutual funds, what types of funds will you select? Why?

Chapter 15: Asset Allocation

Goals
1. Ensure that your current asset allocation is appropriate.
2. Determine a plan for future allocation.

Analysis
1. Enter information about your current investments in the following chart:

CATEGORY	MARKET VALUE OF INVESTMENT	GOAL(S) MET BY	PROPORTION OF FUNDS ALLOCATED TO THIS INVESTMENT
Large Cap Stock			
Mid Cap Stock			
Small Cap Stock			
International			
Retail			
Banking/Finance			
Manufacturing			
Bonds/Corp.			
Bonds/Gov't			
REIT			
Technology			
Other			
Other			
Other			
Total Investments			

Decisions
1. Is your current asset allocation appropriate? If not, what changes will you make to better diversify your investments?

2. As you make additional investments in the future, how do you plan on allocating your assets?

Chapter 16: Auto, Homeowner's, and Health Insurance

Goals
1. Ensure that your property and health are covered by insurance.
2. Determine whether you should increase insurance levels in the future.

Analysis
1. Review the personal balance sheet you created in chapter 2. Which assets require insurance?

2. What are your health insurance needs? Is health insurance available through your employer? If so, what plan is best suited to your needs (e.g., HMO or PPO)?

3. In the following chart, log each insurance need you have identified. At www.worldinsurance.com, obtain premium quotes for each risk exposure.

RISK EXPOSURE	PROVIDED BY SELF/EMPLOYER/OTHER	PREMIUM
	TOTAL PREMIUMS	

4. Compare what the total money insurance premiums will cost you to the amount budgeted in your personal cash flow statement. Revise your personal cash flow statement, if necessary. If your premiums are higher than expected, what actions can you take (e.g., increasing deductibles)?

Personal Cash Flow Statement

Cash Inflows	This Month
Disposable (after-tax) income	_____
Interest on deposits	_____
Dividend payments	_____
Other	_____
Total Cash Inflows	_____
Cash Outflows	
Rent	_____
Cable TV	_____
Electricity and water	_____
Telephone	_____
Groceries	_____
Health care insurance and expenses	_____
Clothing	_____
Car expenses (insurance, maintenance, and gas)	_____
Recreation	_____
Other	_____
Total Cash Outflows	_____
Net Cash Flows	_____

Decisions

1. What steps have you taken or will you take to ensure that your property and health are adequately insured?

2. What future events will prompt you to reevaluate your insurance needs? What changes do you anticipate making?

Chapter 17: Life Insurance

Goals
1. Determine whether you need to purchase life insurance and if so, how much.
2. Determine the most appropriate types of life insurance.
3. Decide whether you should purchase or add to life insurance in the future.

Analysis
1. Identify your insurance needs by completing the following template. Estimate dollar amounts for each need.

Life Insurance Needs Analysis

Final expenses (funeral and other related items)   _____

Transition funds for spouse   _____

Funds for education, child care, and other:

    Child one   _____

    Child two   _____

    Child three   _____

    Child four   _____

    Child five   _____

    Total   _____

Funds to meet parental needs (Medical, nursing home, etc.)

Other   _____

Other   _____

Other   _____

Other   _____

Total   _____

Life insurance provided by employer   _____

Coverage needed *   _____

* This is the amount for which you should obtain quotes.

2. Review the following information about types of life insurance plans. Indicate how suitable each type is for your situation in the right-hand column.

Type of Insurance Plan	Benefits	Suitability
Term Insurance	Insurance benefits provided to beneficiary	
Whole-Life Insurance	Insurance benefits provided to beneficiary and policy builds a cash value over time	
Universal Insurance	Insurance benefits provided to beneficiary and policy builds a cash value over time	

3. If you have determined that you need life insurance, obtain premiums for the policy type and amount you desire at www.selectquote.com

```




```

Make any necessary changes to your personal cash flow statement.

Personal Cash Flow Statement

Cash Inflows	**This Month**
Disposable (after-tax) income	_____
Interest on deposits	_____
Dividend payments	_____
Other	_____
Total Cash Inflows	_____
Cash Outflows	
Rent	_____
Cable TV	_____
Electricity and water	_____
Telephone	_____
Groceries	_____
Health care insurance and expenses	_____
Clothing	_____
Car expenses (insurance, maintenance, and gas)	_____
Recreation	_____
Other	_____
Total Cash Outflows	_____
Net Cash Flows	_____

Decisions

1. Do you need life insurance? If so, how much and what type will suit your needs?

```




```

2. What do you anticipate your life insurance coverage needs to be in the future?

```




```

Chapter 18: Retirement Planning

Goals
1. Ensure an adequate financial position at the time you retire.
2. Reduce the tax liability on your present income.

Analysis
1. At www.msn.com, click on the tab "Money." Scroll to the bottom of the page and click on "Site Map." On the site map, click on "Retirement and Wills." Use the calculator to determine how much savings you will need to retire.
2. The next step is to determine how much money you must save per year, the return you must earn, and the savings period to meet your goal for retirement savings. Experiment with different inputs in the following calculator.

Present Value of an Annuity

Payment per Period	
Number of Periods	
Interest Rate per Period	
Present Value	

Make any necessary adjustments to your personal cash flow statement.

Personal Cash Flow Statement

Cash Inflows	This Month
Disposable (after-tax) income	
Interest on deposits	
Dividend payments	
Other	
Total Cash Inflows	
Cash Outflows	
Rent	
Cable TV	
Electricity and water	
Telephone	
Groceries	
Health care insurance and expenses	
Clothing	
Car expenses (insurance, maintenance, and gas)	
Recreation	
Other	
Total Cash Outflows	
Net Cash Flows	

3. When examining retirement plans, keep in mind that tax benefits are important criteria. In the right-hand column of the following table, indicate how suitable the plan options are for you.

Type of Retirement Plan	Benefits	Suitability
Employer's Retirement Plan	Employee contributions are tax-deferred; employer may match contributions	
Traditional IRA or Roth IRA	Contribute up to $2,000 per year (tax-deferred) to a traditional IRA. Alternatively, contribute up to $2,000 annually to a Roth IRA after taxes; the withdrawal at retirement will not be taxed.	
Annuities	Contribute money to an annuity to supplement any other retirement plan. The only tax advantage is that any income earned on the investment is not taxed until withdrawal at retirement.	

4. Use the 401(K) planner template to see how your savings can grow.

401(K) Planner

401(K) Contribution per paycheck	
401(K) Employer match per paycheck	
Paychecks per year (12, 24, 26, and 52)	
Expected annual rate of return	
Age as of the end of this tax year	
Anticipated retirement age	
Current value of 401(K)	
Date (the "as of" date for the current value)	
Enter the date of the year end	
Marginal Tax Rate (State plus Federal)	

Tax Deferred 401K Plan Growth

Age	Estimated 401K Value
30	
35	
45	
65	

Taxable Savings Plan Growth

Age	Estimated Savings Value
30	
35	
45	
65	

Pre-tax retirement income

From retirement age to 90 years old Monthly Income

Pre-tax retirement income

From retirement age to 90 years old Monthly Income

Decisions

1. How much savings do you need to support you during retirement? [   ]

2. How much will you contribute to your retirement? What type of plan(s) will you contribute to?

[   ]

3. What are the present-day tax savings from your retirement planning? [   ]

Chapter 19: Estate Planning

Goals
1. Create a will.
2. Establish a plan for trusts or gifts if your estate is subject to high taxes.
3. Decide whether to create a living will or assign power of attorney.

Analysis
1. At the msn.com Web site, learn more about how equipped you are to create your own will by taking the "make-a-will quiz." Click on the tab "Money" and then go to the site map where you will see the quiz.
2. Determine the size of your estate by reviewing your personal balance sheet and filling out the table below.

Gross Estate	Amounts
Cash	
Stocks and bonds	
Notes and mortgages	
Annuities	
Retirement benefits	
Personal residence	
Other real estate	
Insurance	
Automobiles	
Artwork	
Jewelry	
Other (furniture, collectibles, etc.)	
Gross Estate	

3. Next, consider the following estate planning issues. Indicate your action plan in the right-hand column.

Issue	Status
Possible heirs and executor to my estate?	
Tax implications on my estate?	
Are trusts and gifts needed?	
Power of attorney necessary?	
Durable power of attorney necessary?	

Decisions

1. Will you create a will on your own or with an attorney's assistance? What special stipulations (for an heir or executor, or donations to charity) will you include?

2. Do you need to establish trusts or gifts to reduce your estate's tax liability?

3. Will you assign power of attorney and/or durable power of attorney?

Chapter 20: Integrating the Components of a Financial Plan

Goals
1. Review your completed financial plan.
2. Record your asset locations.

Analysis
1. Congratulations! You've now completed your financial plan. Remember that financial planning is an ongoing task. Use the following table as a reminder to review key parts of your financial plan

ITEM	WHEN REVIEWED	DATE OF REVIEW
Short-term goals	As needed	
Intermediate-term goals	Annually	
Long-term goals	Annually	
Personal cash flow statement	Annually	
Personal balance sheet	Annually	
Tax situation	Annually, before year end	
Selection of financial institution	Biannually	
Credit report	Annually	
Loans	As needed	
Risk tolerance	Every 2-3 years	
Portfolio and asset allocation including stocks, bonds, and money market instruments	Annually	
Property and casualty insurance needs	Annually	
Life insurance needs	As dictated by critical events	
Retirement plan	Annually	
Will and estate planning	As dictated by critical events	

2. Now that your plan is complete, store it for safekeeping. Along with your financial plan, keep a record of the location of your key assets and financial documents. Use the following template as a guide.

Location of Important Documents

Estate Related	Location
Wills / Trusts	
Letter of Last Instruction	
Other	
Other	

Insurance	
Life	
Health	
Disability	
Auto	
Other	
Other	

Certificates and Deeds	
Automobile Titles	
Real Estate Deeds	
Birth Certificates	
Marriage Certificate	
Passports	
Other	
Other	

Investments And Savings	
Certificates of Deposit	
Stock Certificates	
Passbooks	
Mutual Fund Records	
Other	
Other	

Tax Records	
Last Year's Tax Return	
Last 7 Years of Tax Records	
Other	
Other	

Loans And Credit Cards	
Loan Notes (still outstanding)	
List of Credit Card Numbers	
Other	
Other	

The Sampson Family: A Continuing Case

Chapter 1: Overview of a Financial Plan

Case Questions

1. Help the Sampsons summarize their current financial position, their goals, and their plans for achieving their goals by filing out the following templates.

CURRENT FINANCIAL POSITION

Major Assets	Amount
Savings (High, Medium, or Low)	
Money Owed	
Salary	

FINANCIAL GOALS

	Goal 1. Purchase new car for Sharon this year	Goal 2. Pay for children's college education in 12-17 years from now	Goal 3. Set aside money for retirement
How to Achieve the Goal			
How to Implement the Plan			
How to Evaluate the Plan			

Chapter 2: Planning with Personal Financial Statements

Case Questions

1. Using the information in the text, prepare a personal cash flow statement for the Sampsons.

Personal Cash Flow Statement

Cash Inflows   **This Month**

_____   _____

_____   _____

_____   _____

_____   _____

Total Cash Inflows   _____

Cash Outflows

_____   _____

_____   _____

_____   _____

_____   _____

_____   _____

_____   _____

_____   _____

_____   _____

_____   _____

_____   _____

Total Cash Outflows   _____

Net Cash Flows   _____

2. Based on their personal cash flow statement, will the Sampsons be able to meet their savings goals? If not, how do you recommend that they revise their personal cash flow statement in order to achieve their savings goals?

3. Prepare a personal balance sheet for the Sampsons.

Personal Balance Sheet

Assets

Liquid Assets	
Cash	
Checking account	
Savings account	
Total liquid assets	
Household Assets	
Home	
Car	
Furniture	
Total household assets	
Investment Assets	
Stocks	
Bonds	
Mutual Funds	
Total investment assets	
Total Assets	

Liabilities and Net Worth	
Current Liabilities	
Loans	
Credit card balance	
Total current liabilities	
Long-Term Liabilities	
Mortgage	
Car loan	
Total long-term liabilities	
Total Liabilities	

Net Worth	

4. What is the Sampsons' net worth? Based on the personal cash flow statement that you prepared in question 2, do you expect that their net worth will increase or decrease in the future? Why?

Chapter 3: Applying Time Value Concepts

Case Questions

1. Help the Sampsons determine how much they will have for the children's education by calculating how much $3,600 in annual savings will accumulate to if they earn interest of (a) 5 percent and (b) 7 percent. Next, determine how much $4,800 in annual savings will accumulate to if they earn interest of (a) 5 percent and (b) 7 percent.

Savings Accumulated Over the Next 12 Years (Based on Plan to Save $3,600 per Year)

Amount Saved Per Year	$3,600	$3,600
Interest Rate	5%	7%
Years	12	12
Future Value of Savings		

Savings Accumulated Over the Next 12 Years (Based on Plan to Save $4,800 per Year)

Amount Saved Per Year	$4,800	$4,800
Interest Rate	5%	7%
Years	12	12
Future Value of Savings		

2. What is the impact of the higher interest rate of 7 percent on the Sampsons' accumulated savings?

3. What is the impact of the higher savings of $4,800 on their accumulated savings?

4. If the Sampsons set a goal to save $70,000 for their children's college education in 12 years, how would you determine the yearly savings necessary to achieve this goal? How much would they have to save by the end of each year to achieve this goal, assuming a 5 percent annual interest rate?

Calculator: Savings Needed Each Year

Future Value	$70,000
Interest Rate	5%
Years	12
Savings Needed Each Year	

Chapter 4: : Using Tax Concepts for Planning

Case Questions

1. Help the Sampsons estimate their federal income taxes for this year by preparing the following template.

Gross Income   _____

Retirement Plan Contribution   _____

Adjusted Gross Income   _____

Deductions

      Interest Expense   _____

      Real Estate Taxes   _____

      Contributions   _____   _____

Exemptions ($2,800 each)   _____

Taxable Income   _____

Tax Rate   _____

Tax Liability   _____

Chapter 5: Banking and Interest Rates

Case Questions

1. Advise the Sampsons on the maturity to select when investing their savings in a CD for a down payment on a car. What are the advantages or disadvantages of the relatively short-term maturities versus the longer-term maturities?

2. Advise the Sampsons on the maturity to select when investing their savings for their children's education. Describe any advantages or disadvantages of the relatively short-term maturities versus the longer-term maturities.

3. If you thought that interest rates were going to rise in the next few months, how might this affect the advice that you give the Sampsons?

Chapter 6: Managing Your Money

Case Questions

1. Review the Sampsons' recent cash flow statement and their personal balance sheet from Chapter 2 and offer them advice on how they can improve their liquidity situation.

1. Based on the cash flow statement and personal balance sheet, do the Sampsons have adequate liquidity? If not, what level of savings should they maintain for liquidity purposes?

2. Advise the Sampsons on money market investments they should consider to provide them with adequate liquidity.

Chapter 7: Managing Your Credit

Case Questions

1. Compare the amount of interest that the Sampsons are earning on their savings and paying on their credit card debt by completing the following template.

Savings

Interest rate earned on savings	5%
Savings balance	
Annual interest earned on savings	

Paying Off Credit Balance

Interest rate paid on credit	18%
Credit balance	
Annual interest paid on credit	

2. Advise the Sampsons on whether they should continue making minimum payments on their credit card or use money from their savings to pay off the credit balance.

3. Explain how the Sampsons' credit card decisions are related to their budget.

Chapter 8: Personal Loans

Case Questions

1. Advise the Sampsons on possible loan maturities. Go to http://loan.yahoo.com/a/autocalc.html and click on "Loan Payment Calculator." Input information to determine the possible monthly car payments for a three-year (36-month) payment period, a four-year (48-month) payment period, and a five-year (60-month) period. Enter the results in the following table.

	Three-Year (36-month) Periods	Four-Year (48-month) Periods	Five-Year (60-month) Periods
Interest rate			
Monthly payment			
Total finance charges			
Total payments including the down payment and the trade-in			

2. What are the tradeoffs among the three alternative loan maturities?

3. Based on the information on finance payments that you retrieved from the loan payment Web site, advise the Sampsons on the best loan maturity for their needs.

Chapter 9: Purchasing and Financing a Home

Case Questions

1. Determine the monthly mortgage payment (excluding property taxes and insurance) on a $90,000 mortgage if the Sampsons obtain a new 30-year at the 8 percent interest rate.

Mortgage loan	$90.000
Interest rate	8%
Years	30
Loan payment	

2. The Sampsons expect that they will not move for at least three years. Advise the Sampsons on whether they should refinance their mortgage by comparing the savings of refinancing with the costs.

Current mortgage payment	
New mortgage payment	
Monthly savings	
Annual savings	
Marginal tax rate	
Increase in taxes	
Annual savings after-tax	
Years in house after refinancing	
Total savings	

3. Why might your advice about refinancing change in the future?

Chapter 10: Basics for Investing in Stocks

Case Questions

1. Compare the returns from investing in bank CDs to the possible returns from stock over the next 12 years by filling in the following template:

Savings Accumulated Over the Next 12 Years

	Certificate of Deposit	Weak Stock Market	Strong Stock Market
Amount invested			
Annual return			
FVIFA			
Value of investments in 12 years			

2. Explain to the Sampsons why there is a tradeoff when investing in bank CDs versus stock to support their children's future college education.

3. Advise the Sampsons on whether they should invest their money each month in bank CDs in stocks, or in some combination to save for their children's college education.

Chapter 11: Return and Risk from Investing in Stocks

Case Questions

1. Advise the Sampsons as to whether they should put all of their investments in technology stocks.

2. Should the information the Sampsons read on the Web site affect how they invest in stocks?

Chapter 12: How to Purchase Stocks

Case Questions

1. Offer advice to the Sampsons on whether they should buy the stocks based on the information on the Web site.

2. Other Web sites identify firms that were top performers the previous day. Should the Sampsons buy these stocks? Explain.

Chapter 13: Investing in Bonds

Case Questions

1. Should the Sampsons consider investing a portion of their savings in bonds to save for their children's education? Why or why not?

2. If the Sampsons should purchase bonds, what maturities should they consider, keeping in mind their investment goal?

3. If the Sampsons should consider bonds, should they invest in corporate bonds or municipal bonds? Factor the return they would receive after tax liabilities into your analysis, based on the bonds having a $1,000 par value and the Sampsons being in a 28 percent marginal tax bracket.

After Tax Rate

Corporate bond yield	
Marginal tax rate	
After Tax Rate	
Annual interest ($)	

Chapter 14: Investing in Mutual Funds

Case Questions

1. Why might mutual funds be more appropriate investments for the Sampsons than individual stocks or bonds?

2. Should the Sampsons invest their savings in mutual funds?

3. What types of mutual funds should the Sampsons consider, given their investment objective?

Chapter 15: Asset Allocation

Case Questions

1. Advise the Sampsons regarding the soundness of their tentative decision to invest all of their children's college education money in a biotechnology mutual fund.

2. The Sampsons are aware that diversification is important. Therefore, they have decided that they will initially invest in one biotechnology mutual fund and then invest in three other biotechnology mutual funds as they accumulate more money. In this way, even if one mutual fund performs poorly, they expect that the other biotechnology mutual funds will perform well. How can the Sampsons diversify their investments more effectively?

Chapter 16: Auto, Homeowner's, and Health Insurance

Case Questions

1. Advise the Sampsons regarding their car insurance. Do they have enough insurance? Do they have too much insurance? How might they be able to reduce their premium?

2. Consider the Sampsons homeowner's insurance. Do they have enough insurance? Do they have too much insurance? Is increasing their deductible well advised?

3. Make suggestions to the Sampsons regarding their health insurance. Do they have enough insurance? Do they have too much insurance?

4. Should the Sampsons have disability insurance? Why or why not?

Chapter 17: Life Insurance

Case Questions

1. Determine the present value of the insurance benefits that could provide $40,000 over the next 15 years for the Sampson family. Assume that the insurance payment could be invested to earn 6 percent interest over time.

Annual amount	$40,000
Number of years	15
Annual interest rate	6%
Present value	

2. Considering the insurance benefits needed to provide $40,000 over the next 15 years, plus the additional $330,000 of insurance coverage, what amount of insurance coverage is needed?

3. Given the amount of insurance coverage needed and Dave's present age (30 years old), estimate the premium that the Sampsons would pay using one of the insurance Web sites mentioned in the chapter (such as http://insweb.com).

Chapter 18: Retirement Planning

Case Questions

1. If Dave and his employer contribute a total of $10,000, how much would that amount accumulate to over the next 30 years when Dave and his wife hope to retire?

Contribution	$10,000
Years	30
Annual rate of return	
Future Value	

2. Assuming that Dave's marginal tax bracket is 28 percent, by how much should his federal taxes decline this year if he contributes $7,000 to his retirement account?

3. Assuming that Dave contributes $7,000 to his retirement account and that his taxes are lower as a result, by how much are Dave's cash flows reduced over one year? (Refer to your answer in question 2 when solving this problem.)

4. If Dave contributes $7,000 to his retirement, he will have less cash inflows as a result. How could the Sampsons afford to make this contribution? Suggest some ways that they may be able to offset the reduction in cash inflows by reexamining the cash flow statement you created for them in chapter 2.

Chapter 19: Estate Planning

Case Questions

1. Advise the Sampsons on how they can plan their estate to achieve their financial goals.

2. What important consideration are the Sampsons overlooking in their estate planning goals?

Chapter 20: Integrating the Components of a Financial Plan

Case Questions

1. Explain how the Sampsons' budgeting affects all of their other financial planning decisions.

2. How are the Sampsons' liquidity and investment decisions related?

3. In what ways are the Sampsons' financing and investing decisions related?

4. Explain how the Sampsons' retirement planning decisions are related to their investing decisions.

5. How likely is it that the Sampsons will achieve their financial goals, now that they have captured them in a financial plan? What activity must they periodically undertake?

Brad Brooks: A Continuing Case

Part 1: Tools for Financial Planning

Case Questions

1. a. Prepare personal financial statements for Brad, including a personal cash flow statement and personal balance sheet.

Personal Cash Flow Statement

Cash Inflows	This Month
Total Cash Inflows	
Cash Outflows	
Total Cash Outflows	
Net Cash Flows	

Personal Balance Sheet

Assets

Liquid Assets	
Cash	
Checking account	
Savings account	
Other liquid assets	
Total liquid assets	
Household Assets	
Home	
Car	
Furniture	
Other household assets	
Total household assets	
Investment Assets	
Stocks	
Bonds	
Mutual Funds	
Other investments	
Total investment assets	
Total Assets	

Liabilities and Net Worth

Current Liabilities	
Loans	
Credit card balance	
Other current liabilities	
Total current liabilities	
Long-Term Liabilities	
Mortgage	
Car loan	
Other long-term liabilities	
Total long-term liabilities	
Total Liabilities	

Net Worth	

b. Based on these statements, make specific recommendations to Brad as to what he needs to do to achieve his goals of paying off his credit card balance and saving for retirement.

c. What additional goals could you recommend to Brad for both the short and long-term?

2. Consider Brad's goal to retire in 20 years by saving $4,000 per year starting five years from now.

a. Based on your analysis of Brad's cash flow and your recommendations, is saving $4,000 per year a realistic goal? If not, what other goal would you advise?

b. In order for Brad to know what his $4,000 per year will accumulate to in 20 years, what additional assumption (or piece of information) must he make (or have)?

c. Assuming that Brad invests the $4,000 per year for 20 years in something that will return 12 percent, how much will he have at that time?

Future Value of an Annuity

Payment per Period	$4,000
Number of Periods	20
Interest Rate per Period	12%
Future Value	

d. How much will it cost Brad to wait five years to start investing? How much additional funds will Brad have to save each year to end up with the same amount that he would have if he started saving now instead of five years from now? (Again assume a 12 percent annual return.)

Future Value of an Annuity

Payment per Period	$4,000
Number of Periods	15
Interest Rate per Period	12%
Future Value	

3. Develop three or four suggestions that could help Brad reduce his income tax exposure.

Suggestions to Reduce Taxes	Pros	Cons

4. Would any of your recommendations in questions 1 through 3 change if Brad were 45? If he were 60? Why or why not?

5. Prepare a written or oral report on your findings and recommendations to Brad.

Part 2: Managing Your Liquidity

Case Questions

1. Assuming that you could convince Brad to maintain checking, savings, and retirement accounts, discuss the pros and cons of various types of financial institutions where Brad could maintain his:

    a. checking account.
    b. savings account.
    c. retirement accounts.

    Be sure to comment on Brad's idea to find financial institutions that can give him advice on his financial decisions.

2. If Brad's stocks double in value over the next five years, what annual return would he realize? (Hint: Use the future value table.) Based on his projected annualized return would it be advisable to sell the stocks to pay off his credit card? Should Brad consider shopping for a new credit card?

3. How would you address Brad's reluctance to pay off his credit card balance? Show him what he could earn in five years if he paid it off and invested the interest saved at 6 percent.

Future Value of a Lump Sum

Yearly Savings	
Number of Periods	
Interest Rate per Period	
Future Value	

4. Would your advice change if Brad were:
   a. 45 years old?
   b. 60 years old?

5. Prepare a written or oral report on your findings and recommendations for Brad.

Part 3: Personal Financing

Case Questions

1. Refer to Brad's personal cash flow statement that you developed in Part 1. Recompute his expenses to determine if Brad can afford to:

    a. Purchase the new car.
    b. Lease a new car.
    c. Purchase his condo.
    d. Purchase both the car and condo.
    e. Lease the car and purchase the condo.

Personal Cash Flow Statement

Cash Inflows   **This Month**

_____   _____

_____   _____

_____   _____

_____   _____

Total Cash Inflows

Cash Outflows

_____   _____

_____   _____

_____   _____

_____   _____

_____   _____

_____   _____

_____   _____

_____   _____

_____   _____

Total Cash Outflows

Net Cash Flows

2. What are the advantages and disadvantages to Brad of leasing rather than purchasing a car?

3. Based on the information you provided, Brad decides not to buy the condo at this time. How can he save the necessary funds to purchase a condo or house in the future? Be specific in your recommendations.

Future Value of an Annuity

Payment per Period	
Number of Periods	
Interest Rate per Period	
Future Value	

4. How would your advice to Brad differ if he were:

   a. 45 years old?
   b. 60 years old?

5. Prepare a written or oral report on your findings and recommendations to Brad.

Part 4: Personal Investing

Case Questions

1. Comment on each of the following elements of Brad's plan:

   a. Level of diversification with three Internet stocks.
   b. View on bonds and not including them in his portfolio.
   c. Trading on-line.
   d. Margin trading.
   e. Source of information, I.e., "hot tips"

2. With Brad's lack of knowledge of investing and limited time to learn or do research, what might be the best option for Brad to pursue and still get the benefit of the growth in Internet investing?

3. What factors will influence Brad's asset allocation? Based on these factors, what might be a suitable sample portfolio for Brad?

4. How would your answer to the sample portfolio part of question three be affected if Brad were:
   a. 45 years old?
   b. 60 years old?

5. Prepare a written or oral report on your findings and recommendations to Brad.

Part 5: Protecting Your Wealth

Case Questions

1. Concerning Brad's insurance plan, comment on:

   a. Using the whole-life policy's loan feature as a means of maintaining liquidity.
   b. His need for life insurance.
   c. If you see any reason for life insurance in "b," is whole-life the best way to meet it?

2. With regard to Brad's revised retirement plans, show Brad:

   a. What he will have in 30 years if he invests $300 per month at 8%.

Future Value of an Annuity

Payment per year	
Number of years	30
Annual interest rate	8%
Future Value	

   b. How much will he have to save per month at 8% to reach his $500,000 goal in 20 years? In 30 years?

Amount to be Accumulated	$500,000
Number of Years	20
Annual Interest Rate	8%
Annual Deposit	
Monthly Deposit	

Amount to be Accumulated	$500,000
Number of Years	30
Annual Interest Rate	8%
Annual Deposit	
Monthly Deposit	

c. What could be the impact on Brad's current standard of living by retiring 10 years earlier?

d. What would be the impact on his retirement savings if he takes advantage of his employer's match (assume 8%) in 20 years? In 30 years?

Future Value of an Annuity

Payment per year	
Number of years	20
Annual interest rate	8%
Future Value	

Future Value of an Annuity

Payment per year	
Number of years	30
Annual interest rate	8%
Future Value	

e. What other options are available to Brad to save for his retirement? Give the pros cons of each.

3. If Brad really wishes to provide for his nephews' college education, how can a will help him achieve that goal? What else might Brad consider to assure his nephews' college education?

4. Would your advice in question 1-3 change if Brad were:

a. 45 years old?
b. 60 years old?

5. Prepare a written or oral report on your findings and recommendations to Brad.